The Lutheran Course
Workbook

Augsburg Fortress
Minneapolis

Thank you to all the congregations, pastors, group leaders, and adult learners
who contributed to this project by requesting a course like this or field-testing
the material.

Writers: Mark D. Johns, Hans Wiersma
Editors: Gloria E. Bengtson, Laurie J. Hanson, Rebecca Lowe, Kristofer Skrade
Cover Design: Laurie Ingram
Interior Design: Rebecca Lowe
Cover Art: Spunk Design Machine
Interior Art: Brenda Brown

ISBN 0-8066-5278-0

Also available:
The Lutheran Handbook. ISBN 0-8066-5179-2
The Lutheran Course Leader Book. ISBN 0-8066-5277-2
The Lutheran Course Starter Kit. ISBN 0-8066-5279-9
The Lutheran Course DVD. ISBN 0-8066-5276-4

The paper used in this publication meets the minimum requirements of Ameri-
can National Standard for Information Sciences—Permanence of Paper for
Printed Library Materials, ANSI Z329.48-1984.

Manufactured in the U.S.A.

15   14   13   12   11   10   11   12   13   14   15

CONTENTS

ABOUT THE LUTHERAN COURSE

The story of this course begins with *The Lutheran Handbook* (Augsburg Fortress, 2005), a field guide to church stuff, everyday stuff, and Bible stuff. The handbook is a guide to Lutheran theology and culture, as well as the innovative learner resource for Here We Stand confirmation. Nearly 90,000 copies were sold in the first six months after its release. Confirmation students, teachers, and pastors read the handbook and told parents and others about it. Adults read the handbook and started asking, "Is there a course for us that's based on *The Lutheran Handbook?*"

Well, you asked for it and here it is—The Lutheran Course!

ABOUT "WINKING LUTHER"

If you haven't read or seen *The Lutheran Handbook* yet, don't worry. The icon of Martin Luther winking at the reader gives you a glimpse into the handbook and The Lutheran Course.

Luther's theology is grounded in paradoxes—sinner/saint, law/gospel, hidden/revealed—and illuminated by a down-to-earth, everyday sense of humor. "Winking Luther" combines the serious, formal scholarship that was his life's work with the humor and lightheartedness that characterized his personality.

The wink on Luther's face indicates that, even though theology is serious stuff, we should nonetheless remember that it is not our theology that saves us, but Jesus Christ. Our life in the church, therefore, can be buoyant, and our theological wranglings can be done with a sense of humor and love for our neighbor.

INTRODUCTION

The family reunion
Mark D. Johns

When I was a kid, a highlight of the summer was the family reunion at Grandpa and Grandma's house. There were cousins running and chasing all over the place! Grandma coordinated tons of food, and Grandpa's main job was teasing grandkids. The grown-ups mostly sat and talked, and shared news of what was happening in their lives, at home, at work, and in their churches.

The family reunion was a great time, but it was on the way home, with just our little nuclear (but not radioactive) family in the car, that we could talk about what had happened and give the experience some perspective. "Why was Aunt Debra crying so much?" "How come Cousin Fred always has to have his own way?" "Did you see how much beer Uncle Jon was drinking?" On the ride home my parents would try, patiently and simply, to explain very large, grown-up things—like what an alcoholic is, and what a divorce is all about, and how those things cause struggles for children. On the ride home we would laugh again at Grandpa's jokes, compare experiences, and giggle about how Cousin Jen held hands with her new boyfriend the whole day.

The family reunion was a wonderful experience. The ride home was a dialog and conversation in which all that we had seen and heard and experienced was discussed until it began to make some sense.

The Lutheran Course, like a family reunion, is designed to include both the whole family gathering and the ride home.

The large group gathering is energized. It begins light and lively, then may even get a bit rowdy, especially if you've got a good song leader. Next, the large group gathering settles down to business—listening to Grandpa's stories. In this case, "Grandpa" is one of the teachers of the faith who visits electronically on video (despite the fact that not all of them are male, nor are all of them old enough to be grandparents).

In the ride home, with a smaller group of people, you have the opportunity to get to know one another well, to trust one another, and, perhaps on a good day, even to love one another just a bit. Make sure everyone gets a chance to speak up or ask questions. The whole point of the ride home is that everyone talks, everyone listens, and you respond to one another.

So relax, have fun. Come to the reunion. Eat a little, sing a little, laugh a whole lot. Enjoy yourself and enjoy the company of those with whom you are gathering.

What to expect at a session of The Lutheran Course

Table Talk (the gathering)
- Share a meal or refreshments.
- Start talking about the topic for the session.

Large Group Stuff (the "family reunion")
- Sing, listen to Scripture, and pray.
- View a video presentation featuring a well-known Lutheran scholar or speaker.
- Discuss the topic using the Large Group Stuff pages in your Workbook.

Small Group Stuff (the "ride home")
- Discuss the topic using the Small Group Stuff pages in your Workbook.

Wrap-up (the recap)
- Gather with the large group again for a brief closing.

PRESENTERS

James A. Nestingen (Session 1) is Professor of Church History at Luther Seminary, St. Paul, Minnesota, and author of numerous books, including *Martin Luther: His Life and Teachings* (Wipf & Stock, 2004), *Martin Luther: A Life* (Augsburg Books, 2003), and *Manger in the Mountains* (Augsburg Fortress, 1999).

Kenneth Sundet Jones (Session 2) is Assistant Professor of Philosophy and Religion at Grand View College, Des Moines, Iowa, and contributor to *Word and World, The Lutheran Quarterly, The Lutheran Handbook* (Augsburg Fortress, 2005), and Here We Stand confirmation curriculum (Augsburg Fortress).

Winston D. Persaud (Session 3) is Professor of Systematic Theology at Wartburg Seminary, Dubuque, Iowa. His publications include *The Theology of the Cross and Marx's Anthropology: A View from the Caribbean* (Peter Lang, 1991) and numerous articles and essays.

Foster R. McCurley (Session 4) is former Dean of the Faculty and Professor of Old Testament and Hebrew at Lutheran Theological Seminary, Philadelphia, Pennsylvania. His books include *Wrestling with the Word: Christian Preaching from the Hebrew Bible* (Morehouse, 1996).

Barbara R. Rossing (Session 5) is Professor of New Testament at the Lutheran School of Theology, Chicago, Illinois, and author of *The Rapture Exposed: The Message of Hope in the Book of Revelation* (Westview Press, 2005) and *The Choice Between Two Cities: Whore, Bride, and Empire in the Apocalypse* (Trinity Press International, 1999).

Rolf A. Jacobson (Session 6) is Assistant Professor of Old Testament at Luther Seminary, St. Paul, Minnesota, and writer of the No Experience Necessary Bible study series with Kelly A. Fryer.

Kelly A. Fryer (Session 7) is Assistant Professor of Congregational Leadership at Luther Seminary, St. Paul, Minnesota, lead writer of the No Experience Necessary Bible study series, contributing editor of *A Story Worth Sharing: Engaging Evangelism* (Augsburg Fortress, 2004), and author of *Reclaiming the "L" Word: Renewing the Church from Its Lutheran Core* (Augsburg Fortress, 2003).

HOW TO TELL THE DIFFERENCE BETWEEN THE LAW AND THE GOSPEL

"You did not choose me but I chose you."
–John 15:16

❶ Listen for the following essential points in the video:

"Justification by faith" is _____.

Law is an _____ proposition;

Gospel is a _____ fact.

The *opinio legis* is a false belief that _____.

The same Word of God can function as both Law and Gospel,

depending upon _____.

The law accuses and demands.

The gospel liberates and frees us.

2 In what way can you hear Law and Gospel in each of these scriptures?

	LAW	GOSPEL
Genesis 12:1-3	_____	_____
Exodus 20:2-3	_____	_____
Jeremiah 31:31-34	_____	_____
Matthew 9:1-13	_____	_____
John 14:6 and 14:15	_____	_____
Acts 2:37-39	_____	_____
Romans 12:1-2	_____	_____
Revelation 21:22-27	_____	_____

Use the following talking points to get discussion going in your small group. (Note: there's no law that says that you must respond to all of these talking points.) When your discussion time is up, return to the large group.

❶ When driving, how do you react when you see a patrol car?

- ○ I slam on the brakes.
- ○ I check my speedometer.
- ○ I ease off the accelerator.
- ○ I floor it.
- ○ Other _____.

(This question might bring to mind stories about getting pulled over. Share 'em!)

❷ Name some of the "If-then" scenarios you are familiar with in your own life.

(Examples: "If I do my work, then I won't get fired"; "If I eat less and exercise more, then I'll live longer"; "If I raise my children right, then they won't make the same mistakes I made when I was young.")

Write conditions here   Write consequences here

If...   then...

_____   _____

_____   _____

_____   _____

Martin Luther wrote: "I believe that by my own understanding or strength I cannot believe in Jesus Christ my Lord or come to him, but instead the Holy Spirit has called me through the gospel, enlightened me with his gifts, made me holy, and kept me in the true faith."
–The Small Catechism, *Augsburg Fortress, 1996*

We keep God's law, not to earn God's favor,
but out of gratitude that God has already favored us.

❸ Romans 10:9 says: "If you confess with your lips that Jesus is Lord, and believe in your heart that God raised him from the dead, you will be saved."

In which way can this passage be heard as a command?

In which way can it be interpreted as a promise?

If faith is a gift (see Ephesians 2:9), then what does that suggest about the proper way to hear Romans 10?

❹ Reflect upon the following life circumstances. How might the Law speak to them? What would the Gospel say? Which is most helpful to hear?

- You just got promoted.
- You were fired from your job.
- Your teenager earned a scholarship.
- Your teenager was arrested.
- You've just become a new parent.
- Your baby is hospitalized.

As seen in the video commercial, Law & Gospel brand laundry detergent gets out today's tough stains with the dual action of God's Word.

For Session 2 read The Lutheran Handbook, *pages 52–61 and 131–133.*

FIVE THINGS YOU SHOULD KNOW ABOUT THE LUTHERAN REFORMATION

Since we are justified by faith,
we have peace with God through our Lord Jesus Christ.
                                                    –Romans 5:1

❶ Listen for these main points in the video presentation:

In Luther's day, life was _____.

As a monk, young Martin Luther _____.

After Luther was appointed to be a Bible professor, _____.

Because of the newly invented printing press, _____.

At Luther's death he made it clear _____.

What other main point(s) did you hear? _____.

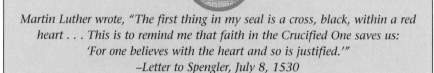

Martin Luther wrote, "The first thing in my seal is a cross, black, within a red heart . . . This is to remind me that faith in the Crucified One saves us:
'For one believes with the heart and so is justified.'"
–Letter to Spengler, July 8, 1530

(For more on Luther's seal, see The Lutheran Handbook, *pp. 82–83.)*

❷ One of Luther's central insights was "the joyful exchange"—that which takes place when Christ unites with a sinner. Fill in the table and determine whether or not this "joyful exchange" is a good deal. Can you add to the lists?

When you are joined to Christ (by grace through faith)	
Jesus gives you his:	in exchange for your:
righteousness	_____
innocence	guilt
blessedness	_____
_____	rebellion
purity	_____
_____	condemnation
life	_____

13

Use the following talking points to get discussion going in your small group. (Note: there's no law that says that you must respond to all of these talking points.) When your discussion time is up, return to the large group.

❶ Turn to pp. 80–81 in *The Lutheran Handbook*. Look at the woodcut of Martin Luther. What sort of person does he look like to you? What personality traits or human qualities do you think the artist was trying to capture and convey? On the map, has anyone ever been to any of the cities named? Have you ever heard of them? If so, in what context? What sorts of places do you imagine them to have been in Luther's day?

❷ Turn to "Seven Important Things That Luther Said . . ." in *The Lutheran Handbook*, pp. 55–57. Which one of the Seven Important Things (ignore number eight for now) do you appreciate most? Which one is the most difficult to understand?

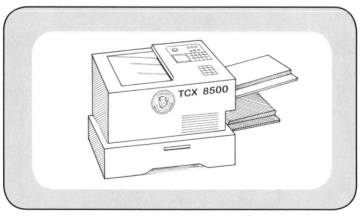

As seen in the video commercial, the breakthrough laser quill technology of the Gutenberg fax-copier-printer is the best thing to happen to reformers like Martin Luther since movable type.

❸ If you could reform the larger church today, where would you begin? (Pick three.)

○ Worship service
○ Worship music
○ Preaching
○ Stewardship
○ Morality
○ Organization
○ Use of technology
○ Biblical literacy
○ Unity
○ Service to others
○ Other: _____

❹ Luther could write some very provocative statements of faith. One of the best-known is the explanation to the Third Article of the Apostles' Creed: "I believe that by my own understanding or strength I cannot believe in Jesus Christ my Lord or come to him" (see *The Lutheran Handbook*, p. 205). These words raise several questions:

- How can I believe that I can't believe?
- If belief doesn't depend upon my own know-how or effort, how do I become a believer?
- Surely I have to exert some kind of effort to be a believer, don't I?

For Session 3 read The Lutheran Handbook, *pages 34–35 and 214–216.*

THE ANATOMY OF A BAPTISM

*"Go therefore and make disciples of all nations,
baptizing them in the name of the Father and of the Son
and of the Holy Spirit."*

–Matthew 28:19

❶ Listen for these main points in the video:

For Lutheran Christians, baptism is _____.

It is absolutely essential to keep two things together: _____
and _____.

Baptism is not about _____, but about _____.

Baptism is a _____ event.

Because of baptism we _____.

God's grace is _____.

What other main point(s) did you hear? _____.

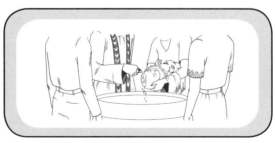

*God is the true actor in baptism, bringing everyone involved to the
font and inspiring trust and faith.*

2 Match the following words about baptism with the biblical figure who said them.

___ "Go therefore and make disciples of all nations, baptizing them in the name of the Father and of the Son and of the Holy Spirit" (Matthew 28:19).

___ "For in the one Spirit we were all baptized into one body . . . and we were all made to drink of one Spirit" (1 Corinthians 12:13).

___ "Repent, and be baptized every one of you in the name of Jesus Christ so that your sins may be forgiven; and you will receive the gift of the Holy Spirit" (Acts 2:38).

___ "I baptize you with water; but one who is more powerful than I is coming . . . He will baptize you with the Holy Spirit and fire" (Luke 3:16).

        A. John the Baptist
        B. Simon Peter
        C. Jesus, the Lord
        D. The apostle Paul

Martin Luther wrote, "[Baptism] brings about forgiveness of sins, redeems from death and the devil, and gives eternal salvation to all who believe it, as the Word and promise of God declare."

–*Small Catechism, in* The Lutheran Handbook, *p. 214*

Use the following talking points to get discussion going in your small group. (Note: there's no law that says that you must respond to all of these talking points.) When your discussion time is up, return to the large group.

❶ Since the human body consists primarily of water, it makes sense that we would be attracted to watery places. Which do you enjoy most: the roar of the ocean, a rushing stream, a quiet mountain lake, a swimming pool, or some other watery place? Why?

❷ Regarding baptism and belief, which of the following best describes you? (Check all that apply. Share your answers with the group.)

○ I was baptized as a baby or child. I don't remember it.
○ I was baptized as a youth or adult. I remember it vividly.
○ I was baptized more than once.
○ I've been a believer for as long as I can remember.
○ I was a believer as a child.
○ I was not much of a believer for a time.
○ I only recently became a believer.
○ I still struggle with my doubts.
○ Other: _____

As seen in the video commercial, Splashy Font brand baptismal napkins come in handy when baptismal waters overflow.

❸ Turn to "The Anatomy of a Baptism" in *The Lutheran Handbook*, pp. 34–35.

- Which of the practices and beliefs about baptism listed here are the most perplexing?
- Which of the practices and beliefs about baptism listed here are the most reassuring?

❹ We are baptized "in the name of the Father, and of the Son, and of the Holy Spirit" and the sign of the cross is made on us (*Lutheran Book of Worship*, pp. 123–124). In his Small Catechism Martin Luther instructs us to make the sign of the cross on ourselves as we begin our prayers, recalling that we are "under the care of the Father, Son, and Holy Spirit" (*The Lutheran Handbook*, pp. 224–225).

- Do you ever make the sign of the cross on yourself in worship or at prayer? (If you're wondering how to do this, see *The Lutheran Handbook*, p. 104.)
- Have you ever associated the sign of the cross with your baptism?
- Are there other ways you remember your baptism in your daily practices?

❺ H_2O fun facts: Which of these are new or surprising to you?

- Without water, life as we know it could not exist.
- Water is the only substance that occurs (at ordinary temperature) in all three states of matter: solid, liquid, gas.
- Water covers three-fourths of the earth's surface (in oceans, lakes, rivers, and swamps).
- Protoplasm—the basic material of living cells—is mostly water.
- 75 to 90 percent of human body weight comes from water.

For Session 4 read The Lutheran Handbook, *pages 36–40 and 222–223.*

HOW TO RECEIVE COMMUNION

While they were eating, Jesus took a loaf of bread,
and after blessing it he broke it, gave it to the disciples, and said,
"Take, eat; this is my body."
Then he took a cup, and after giving thanks he gave it to them, saying,
"Drink from it, all of you."

–Matthew 26:26-27

❶ **Listen for these main points in the video:**

What makes the Lutheran understanding of Holy Communion
unique? _____.

In the Lord's Supper the church proclaims _____.

The best way to receive the sacrament is by _____.

The important words in the sacrament are _____.

The bread and wine are _____.

What you get in the Lord's Supper is _____.

What other main point(s) did you hear? _____.

❷ **The "Words of Institution" used in worship are based on**
Paul's account in 1 Corinthians. The four Gospels also
represent vantage points on what took place "on the
night when he was betrayed." What similarities do you
see in these accounts? What differences are there? Why do
you think these differences exist?

1 Corinthians 11:23-25
The Lord Jesus on the night when he was betrayed took a loaf of bread, and when he had given thanks, he broke it and said, "This is my body that is for you. Do this in remembrance of me." In the same way he took the cup also, after supper, saying, "This cup is the new covenant in my blood. Do this, as often as you drink it, in remembrance of me."

Matthew 26:26-28
While they were eating, Jesus took a loaf of bread, and after blessing it he broke it, gave it to the disciples, and said, "Take, eat; this is my body." Then he took a cup, and after giving thanks he gave it to them, saying, "Drink from it, all of you; for this is my blood of the covenant, which is poured out for many for the forgiveness of sins."

Mark 14:22-24
While they were eating, he took a loaf of bread, and after blessing it he broke it, gave it to them, and said, "Take; this is my body." Then he took a cup, and after giving thanks he gave it to them, and all of them drank from it. He said to them, "This is my blood of the covenant, which is poured out for many."

Luke 22:14-20
When the hour came, he took his place at the table, and the apostles with him. He said to them, "I have eagerly desired to eat this Passover with you before I suffer; for I tell you, I will not eat it until it is fulfilled in the kingdom of God." Then he took a cup, and after giving thanks he said, "Take this and divide it among yourselves; for I tell you that from now on I will not drink of the fruit of the vine until the kingdom of God comes." Then he took a loaf of bread, and when he had given thanks, he broke it and gave it to them, saying, "This is my body, which is given for you. Do this in remembrance of me." And he did the same with the cup after supper, saying, "This cup that is poured out for you is the new covenant in my blood."

John 13:4-5
[Jesus] got up from the table, took off his outer robe, and tied a towel around himself. Then he poured water into a basin and began to wash the disciples' feet and to wipe them with the towel that was tied around him.

Use the following talking points to get discussion going in your small group. (Note: there's no law that says that you must respond to all of these talking points.) When your discussion time is up, return to the large group.

❶ Complete the sentence, "The first time I received the Lord's Supper, I . . ."

❷ Complete the sentence, "One question I've always had about the Lord's Supper is . . ."

❸ The Meal of Bread and Wine is known by many names. ("Lord's Supper" is the only term that is used in the scriptures—in 1 Corinthians 11:20.) Discuss the various names for the meal. What does each term emphasize?

- Lord's Supper
- Eucharist ("Thanksgiving")
- Holy Communion
- Sacrament of the Altar
- Last Supper
- Christ's Passover
- New Covenant (or Testament)
- Memorial Meal
- Other: _____

Martin Luther wrote, "The words 'given for you' and 'shed for you . . . for the forgiveness of sin' show us that forgiveness of sin, life, and salvation are given to us in the sacrament through these words, because where there is forgiveness of sin, there is also life and salvation."

–Small Catechism in The Lutheran Handbook, *p. 223*

❹ *The Lutheran Handbook* contains five pages (pp. 36–40) of instructions concerning "How to Receive Holy Communion." (That's a lot of instructions for a meal that's supposed to be entirely God's action!)

- Which of the listed practices are a part of the way you receive the Lord's Supper?
- Which practices are new to you? Which practices do you think you might want to adopt?

❺ In 1 Corinthians 11:26, the apostle writes that "as often as you eat this bread and drink the cup, you proclaim the Lord's death until he comes." So, in a way, the Lord's Supper is actually an extension of the sermon. Does this have any implications for how often the Lord's Supper should be offered?

❻ How does receiving the Lord's Supper in worship make you feel? How do you feel when you come to worship and the Lord's Supper is *not* celebrated?

As seen in the video commercial, Reconciliation brand communion biscuits bring sinners together in Christ.

For Session 5 read The Lutheran Handbook, *page 156 and pages 134–137.*

THE THREE MOST REBELLIOUS THINGS JESUS DID

"[He] emptied himself, taking the form of a slave,
being born in human likeness.
And being found in human form,
he humbled himself and became obedient
to the point of death—even death on a cross."
–Philippians 2:7-8

❶ **Listen for these main points in the video:**

As Lutherans, we emphasize Jesus' _____.

The ministry of Jesus on earth emphasized _____.

We're missing something if we focus only on _____.

When we welcome Jesus into our hearts _____.

If Jesus isn't still controversial it's because _____.

Jesus was someone who loved to eat, an activity he often undertook with sinners.

❷ Here is what the Apostles' Creed says about Jesus:

I believe in Jesus Christ, his only Son, our Lord.
He was conceived by the power of the Holy Spirit
  and born of the virgin Mary.
He suffered under Pontius Pilate,
  was crucified, died, and was buried.
He descended into hell.
On the third day he rose again.
He ascended into heaven,
  and is seated at the right hand of the Father.
He will come again to judge the living and the dead.

Are the words of this ancient creed complete? Or are there words that one might add to describe the life of Jesus between "born of the Virgin Mary" and "suffered under Pontius Pilate?" Why does this creed leave such a gap? What would Barbara Rossing say about this gap?

❸ Check out "The Second Article: On Redemption" in *The Lutheran Handbook*, p. 204, for Martin Luther's explanation of what Christ's work is all about. How does Luther expand on the Apostles' Creed?

Martin Luther wrote, "If anyone asks, 'What do you believe in the second article [of the Apostles' Creed] about Jesus Christ?' answer as briefly as possible, 'I believe that Jesus Christ, true Son of God, has become my Lord.'"

–The Large Catechism, in The Book of Concord,
(Augsburg Fortress, 2000), p. 434

Use the following talking points to get discussion going in your small group. (Note: there's no law that says that you must respond to all of these talking points.) When your discussion time is up, return to the large group.

❶ As a group, name as many hymns and songs about Jesus as you can. How many do you know? Can you hum any of the tunes right now? Which ones are your favorites?

❷ Can you name any motion pictures or television shows that have depicted Jesus? What "take" on Jesus do such movies or programs offer?

❸ "Who do you say that I am?" is a question Jesus asks of his followers (in Matthew 16, Mark 8, and Luke 9). Discuss one or more of the following responses to Jesus' pressing question.

"There was really only one Christian, and he died on the cross."
 –Friedrich Nietzsche
  The Antichrist, Sect. 39, 1895

"Jesus was all right, but his disciples were thick and ordinary. It's them twisting it that ruins it for me."
 –John Lennon
  London Evening Standard, March 4, 1966

"Jesus was the first socialist, the first to seek a better life for mankind."
 –Mikhail Gorbachev
  London Daily Telegraph, June 16, 1992

"You are the Messiah!"
 –Simon Peter
  Mark 8:29

❹ Luke 24 tells about Jesus encountering two disciples on the road to Emmaus after his death and resurrection. In this account, Jesus is not recognized until the disciples sit down to a meal with him. In what ways have you encountered the risen Christ? In what ways does he remain hidden?

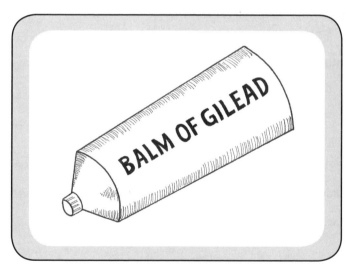

As seen in the video commercial, the Balm of Gilead relieves symptoms of affluenza so you can enjoy faith in Jesus Christ.

For Session 6 read The Lutheran Handbook, *pages 145–146, 168–169, and 175–176.*

HOW TO READ THE BIBLE

Your word is a lamp to my feet and a light to my path.
–Psalm 119:105

How to

❶ Listen for these main points in the video:

In terms of the variety of literature it contains, the Bible can be compared to _____.

literally
figurative
What's different about the way Lutherans read the Bible? _ties in to gospel_ ___ justification by grace through faith. law + gospel.

truth in figurative language
For Lutherans, the Bible's authority comes from _in the reading_ relationship. (c God, HS –) "cradle"

Four hurdles in reading the Bible are:

1. Cultural difference — seek out information — this is where "experts"
2. Assumption a book for experts → balance
3. Contradictions? – ONE GOD / ONE SAVIOR
4. language

Context read

what does this mean?
Three ways to use the Bible effectively are:

- In worship – lectionary – Sunga prayed
- In groups
- to start –

❷ Reflect upon each passage below. Are the words to be understood figuratively or literally? How does the passage proclaim the Gospel of Jesus Christ?

The Bible says:

"In the beginning . . . God created the heavens and the earth."

Genesis 1:1

"The rib that the LORD God had taken from the man he made into a woman."

Genesis 2:22

"The LORD provided a large fish to swallow up Jonah; and Jonah was in the belly of the fish for three days and three nights."

Jonah 1:17

"You are a gracious God and merciful, slow to anger, and abounding in steadfast love, and ready to relent from punishing."

Jonah 4:2

"If your right eye causes you to sin, tear it out and throw it away."

Matthew 5:29

"This is my body, which is given for you. Do this in remembrance of me."

Luke 22:19

"It was nine o'clock in the morning when they crucified him."

Mark 15:25

"For I handed on to you as of first importance what I in turn had received . . . that he was buried, and that he was raised on the third day in accordance with the scriptures."

1 Corinthians 15:3-4

"I am the Alpha and the Omega."

Revelation 22:13

Use the following talking points to get discussion going in your small group. (Note: there's no law that says that you must respond to all of these talking points.) When your discussion time is up, return to the large group.

❶ How would you describe your experience with the Christian Bible? (Check all that apply.)

○ I confess: I am biblically illiterate.
○ I can name the four Gospels.
○ I once started reading the Bible cover to cover, but got bogged down somewhere in the book of Leviticus.
○ I read it at least once a day.
○ I've done some Bible studies in the past.
○ We read it together as a family.
○ I've found that the Bible has provided help for me in times of need.
○ God has spoken to me through the words of scripture.
○ To be honest, I find the Bible difficult to understand.
○ To be honest, I find the Bible not very relevant to present day concerns.
○ Other: _____

❷ Do you have any favorite Bible passages or Bible stories? If you do, share them with your group.

❸ Turn to *The Lutheran Handbook*, pp. 168–169, "The Five Biggest Misconceptions about the Bible." Before this course, did you share any of these misconceptions? Which ones? Is there anything in this list that you aren't quite sure is really a misconception?

Martin Luther wrote, "[God's Word] always awakens new understanding, pleasure, and devotion, and it constantly creates clean hearts and minds. For this Word is not idle or dead, but effective and living."

–The Large Catechism, in The Book of Concord, *(Augsburg Fortress, 2000), p. 400*

❹ Perhaps you've seen this bumper sticker: "God Said It.
I Believe It. That Settles It." Using three-word sentences
ending with "it," what more might be said? (For instance,
"Better Read It" or "Jesus Rules It," etc.)

❺ Jacobson suggested four hurdles and three ways to use the
Bible (see previous pages). What hurdles do you still face?
Which of the three ways to use the Bible have you tried?
With which are you the most comfortable? What way of
experiencing the Bible would you like to try?

*As seen in the video commercial, Hermeneuti-COOL brand magnifying
glasses help you discover the source of a literary work, study its
composition, determine its date, and trace its influence throughout
the ages.*

For Session 7 read The Lutheran Handbook, *pages 89–90 and 105–106.*

HOW TO SHARE YOUR FAITH WITH SOMEONE

people called out to be part in ministry | *pt. is not institution / church / bums in seats*

You will be my witnesses in Jerusalem,
in all Judea and Samaria, and to the ends of the earth.
—Acts 1:8

God's mission in the world — *heal love bless save*

through us to others world / *by grace through faith apart from works*

① Listen for these main points in the video presentation:

Lutherans understand evangelism _in mission to bless loving + blessing_

When you meet Jesus, _Change life - want to share_ .
what happens?? - have you met Jesus?

We can't separate _gift_ from _call_ .
salvation _discipleship_

The church exists _to serve others - for those outside our worship time - to tell the good news / for those not in it yet_

The real truth about evangelists is that they _love people_ .
love God - naturally share

What other main point(s) did you hear? _say you will pray for - write_ .

freedom of a X'n _Get free from sin death devil_ _set free for service to neighbor_

The word "evangelism" is a newer, English word and therefore does not appear in early Lutheran writings, which were written in German and/or Latin. Luther and his fellow reformers, however, referred to their movement as "evangelical." And still today the Lutheran church in Germany is known as the Evangelische Kirche.

❷ Peter, Paul, and Mary: Match these New Testament figures with the place they met the risen Lord and the result.
(WARNING! Being met by Jesus has consequences and may lead to an uncontrollable urge to tell others what you have experienced.)

Figure	Encounter with the Risen Lord	Result
Simon Peter (John 21:1-17, Acts 2:14-40)	A. On the road to Damascus	1. Was the first to tell the good news that Christ is risen
Saul/Paul (Acts 9:1-18)	B. Just outside the empty tomb	2. The first Christian preacher on the day of Pentecost
Mary Magdalene (John 20:11-18)	C. At a breakfast on the beach	3. Was turned from a chief persecutor of Christians into one of Christ's main ambassadors

❸ Here are some common reasons Lutherans give for not being more assertive in sharing the gospel with others.
Check all that seem reasonable to you.

- ○ I'm too shy to talk about religion.
- ○ I'm afraid people will think I'm some sort of religious nut.
- ○ I don't know enough about the Bible.
- ○ I don't want to be like those people who come to my door.
- ○ I don't want to offend anyone.
- ○ Religion is too personal; I don't want to impose it on my friends.
- ○ I don't know how.
- ○ Everyone already knows who Jesus is.
- ○ The church is open every Sunday; people can come if they want.
- ○ What's *your* excuse? _____

Use the following talking points to get discussion going in your small group. (Note: there's no law that says that you must respond to all of these talking points.) When your discussion time is up, return to the large group.

❶ Look at "How to Share Your Faith with Someone" in *The Lutheran Handbook* (pp. 89–90). Which of the seven directives is most daunting for you? Which is most easy to handle?

❷ The word "evangelism" comes from the Greek word *evangel*, which means "good news." (The old English word "Gospel" also means "good news"). Why is the good news about Jesus difficult for many to share? Why is this good news difficult for many to hear?

❸ At the heart of the word "evangelism" you'll find the word "angel." Sometimes in Bible stories good news is brought by supernatural beings (Luke 1:26-38, for example). But technically, an angel is anyone who brings good news. Who are the people who have been angels in bringing the gospel to you? To whom have you been an angel?

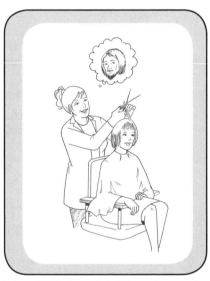

Being an evangelizing Christian should not be confused with being extroverted or loud. Shy, retiring Lutherans are often among the church's most effective evangelizing individuals.

4 Saint Francis of Assisi counseled: "Preach the Gospel at all times. If necessary, use words." How does your congregation proclaim the gospel to others without words? How do you proclaim the gospel to friends and neighbors without words? Do these actions take the place of words? When are words necessary?

5 What's next? This is the final session of The Lutheran Course. But it need not be the final session for your small group. Would there be some benefit if you continued to meet? When and where? How frequently? For what purpose?

As seen in the video commercial, Go Tell It on the Mountain brand Gospel-spreading megaphones get God's Word out to all the world.

SMALL GROUP COVENANT

Our Purpose

The purpose of our small group is to get to know one another, to care for one another, and to support one another as we work together through The Lutheran Course. We will work together to discover, or rediscover, our unique identity as Lutheran Christians. We will strive to help each other grow in faith and deepen our understanding of the gospel.

Our Values

- We agree to make these sessions a top priority in our busy lives, and to attend faithfully.
- We agree to pray for one another, both when we gather and throughout the times between sessions.
- We agree to listen to one another with sensitivity and openness, without passing judgment on others, even if we do not fully agree with them.
- We agree not to give advice unless we are asked.
- We agree to keep personal things spoken in our times together within the circle of our group, maintaining an atmosphere of confidentiality, openness, and trust.
- We agree to freely share with one another our questions, discoveries, struggles, and feelings about topics raised in The Lutheran Course.

Signature _____ Date _____

Group Members

Name   Phone number

_____   _____

_____   _____

_____   _____

_____   _____

_____   _____

_____   _____